Kirk and the Time Machine

Space Base gave Kirk a Time Machine. The Time Machine could send things back in time.

Joe tried the Time Machine on the chips.

The chips became a potato!

Kirk looked at the potato. "Where are my chips?" he said.

"Sorry, sir," said Joe.

Why have the chips become a potato?

Joe looked at the radar. "Sir," said Joe, "there is something on the radar."

Kirk looked at the radar. "Zorgon is coming," he said. "He is coming to steal the Time Machine."

"Sir," said Joe, "I have a plan. I will use the Time Machine to send Zorgon back in time."

Joe turned the Time Machine on Zorgon.

Zorgon began to go back in time!

But Joe could not turn the Time Machine off!

Zorgon went back and back in time.

"Just you wait," said Zorgon. "I will be back! Goo goo ga ga!"

Why is Zorgon a baby?

"Yippee!" said Joe. "I got rid of Zorgon!"

"Yes," said Kirk, "but you have broken the Time Machine."

"Sorry, sir," said Joe.

Quiz

Text Detective

- What was Joe's plan?
- Why did Zorgon say, "Goo goo ga ga"?

Word Detective

- **Phonic Focus:** Initial consonant clusters

  Page 4: Sound out the four phonemes in 'tried'. Can you blend the first two sounds?
- Page 6: Find a word meaning 'rob'.
- Page 7: Can you find three small words in 'Zorgon'?

Super Speller

Read these words:

became   use   began

Now try to spell them!

HA! HA! HA!

Q How do you get a baby astronaut to fall asleep?

A You rock-et.

13

Find out about

- What school was like 50 years ago

Tricky words

- fifty
- ago
- different
- classrooms
- desk
- boring
- chalk
- blackboard

Introduce these tricky words and help the reader when they come across them later!

Text starter

Would you like to go back in time? If you went back fifty years, things in your school would be very different. Classrooms were different, dinners were different – even the toilets were different fifty years ago!

Back in Time

Fifty years ago things in your school were very different.

Classrooms fifty years ago

You had to sit at your desk.
The desks were in rows.

You could not sit by your friends.
It was very boring.

Dinners fifty years ago

Fifty years ago your school dinner was very different.

You **had** to have the school dinner.

You had to eat **all** your dinner.

There were no computers in schools 50 years ago.

Lessons fifty years ago

Fifty years ago your lessons were very different.

The teacher wrote with chalk on the blackboard.

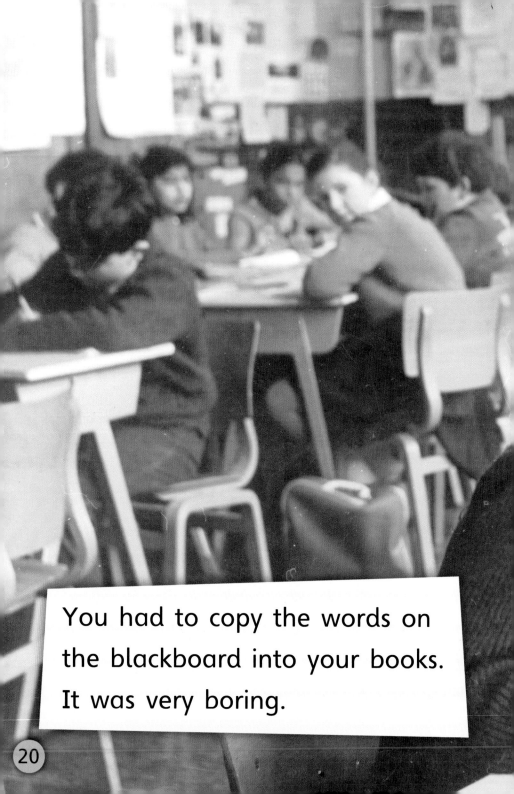

You had to copy the words on the blackboard into your books. It was very boring.

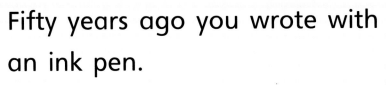

Fifty years ago you wrote with an ink pen.

It could be very difficult.

If your work was messy, you had to do it again and again.

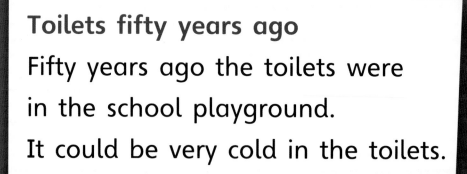

Toilets fifty years ago

Fifty years ago the toilets were
in the school playground.
It could be very cold in the toilets.

The toilets were often very smelly.

1 = 2
2 = 4
3 = 6
4 =
5 =

Fifty years ago you had to learn your tables – just like today!

Quiz

Text Detective

- What happened if your work was messy?
- What do you think was the worst thing about school fifty years ago?

Word Detective

- **Phonic Focus: Initial consonant clusters**

  Page 17: Sound out the six phonemes in 'friends'. Can you blend the first two sounds?
- Page 16: Find a word made from two small words.
- Page 21: Find a word that is the opposite of 'neat'.

Super Speller

Read these words:

today   dinner   again

Now try to spell them!

HA! HA! HA!

 What tables don't you have to learn?

A Dinner tables!

24